this journal belongs to

BARNES
& NOBLE
NEW YORK

my
book
journal
a reading diary
for bibliophiles

U
UNION
SQUARE
& CO.
NEW YORK

Union Square & Co., LLC, is a subsidiary of Sterling Publishing Co., Inc.

ISBN 978-1-4549-4915-2

Printed in Malaysia

2 4 6 8 10 9 7 5 3 1

unionsquareandco.com

Cover design by Jo Obarowski
Interior design by Scott Russo and Christine Heun
Cover and interior images: Shutterstock.com: Franzi
Text written and compiled by Barbara M. Berger

CONTENTS

INTRODUCTION

"I declare after all
there is no enjoyment like reading!
How much sooner one tires
of any thing than of a book!"

—Jane Austen

How to Use *My Book Journal*

This keepsake journal is the perfect place to chronicle your literary journey. Organized into seven parts, you can keep track of what books you've read, what you think about them, and what books you want to read in the future.

Start off with the first section, **Books Read—My Table of Contents.** Once you finish a book, enter its title in the numbered list, and then go to the corresponding numbered page in **My Reading Log.** For example, if the first book you want to enter is *Don Quixote,* you would enter "*Don Quixote*" on the first line of the numbered list on page 6 after the numeral "1." Then you would go to page 12 in My Reading Log, and fill out the page for Title 1 with your review of *Don Quixote* and details about the book. There is space to list 100 books.

You can get some fun ideas about what books to read next in the section called **Book Challenges**. You'll find 24 challenges there that could inspire you to discover some new genres or subjects you've always wanted to try. Check them off in the little boxes as you read them, and fill in your notes on the experience.

My Book Lists is the next section, one that you can complete at your leisure. Create a mini time capsule of your own personal views by filling out 24 lists of your top 10s in a wide range of categories, from your 10 favorite book characters to your 10 favorite book-based movies or TV shows to the 10 scariest books you've read.

Best Book Lists—Prizewinners and Classics contains lists of Modern Library's 100 best fiction and 100 best nonfiction books, as well as a list of the 96 books that have won the Pulitzer Prize for fiction (through 2022), and the 57 books that have won the Booker Prize for fiction (through 2021). There are boxes next to each title that you can check off once you read them (or if you've read them in the past).

The **Book Club** section contains a reading list of 20 titles to get your club started out, along with questions to help facilitate discussion and space for notes.

Finally, the last part, **Wish List of Books to Read**, provides space for you to list the books you want to read in the future.

Happy reading!

BOOKS READ:
MY TABLE OF CONTENTS

BOOK TITLES

1. ______
2. ______
3. ______
4. ______
5. ______
6. ______
7. ______
8. ______
9. ______
10. ______
11. ______
12. ______
13. ______
14. ______
15. ______
16. ______
17. ______
18. ______
19. ______

BOOK TITLES

20. ______

21. ______

22. ______

23. ______

24. ______

25. ______

26. ______

27. ______

28. ______

29. ______

30. ______

31. ______

32. ______

33. ______

34. ______

35. ______

36. ______

37. ______

38. ______

39. ______

40. ______

41. ______

BOOK TITLES

42. __________
43. __________
44. __________
45. __________
46. __________
47. __________
48. __________
49. __________
50. __________
51. __________
52. __________
53. __________
54. __________
55. __________
56. __________
57. __________
58. __________
59. __________
60. __________
61. __________
62. __________
63. __________

BOOK TITLES

64. ____________________
65. ____________________
66. ____________________
67. ____________________
68. ____________________
69. ____________________
70. ____________________
71. ____________________
72. ____________________
73. ____________________
74. ____________________
75. ____________________
76. ____________________
77. ____________________
78. ____________________
79. ____________________
80. ____________________
81. ____________________
82. ____________________
83. ____________________
84. ____________________
85. ____________________

BOOK TITLES

86. ______________________________

87. ______________________________

88. ______________________________

89. ______________________________

90. ______________________________

91. ______________________________

92. ______________________________

93. ______________________________

94. ______________________________

95. ______________________________

96. ______________________________

97. ______________________________

98. ______________________________

99. ______________________________

100. ______________________________

MY READING LOG

"Dreams, books, are each a world;
And books, we know,
Are a substantial world,
both pure and good."

—William Wordsworth

1. TITLE

Start date: ____________ Finish date: ____________

Author(s): ____________

Publisher: ____________ Year published: ____________

Fiction/Genre: ____________ or Nonfiction/Category: ____________

Where I bought, borrowed, or found the book: ____________

Main character(s) or subject: ____________

My review and thoughts:

OVERALL RATING: Quality of writing ☆☆☆☆☆

Strength of characters ☆☆☆☆☆ Plot ☆☆☆☆☆

2. TITLE

Start date: ______________ Finish date: ________________

Author(s): ______________________________________

Publisher: ____________________ Year published: ________

Fiction/Genre: _________ or Nonfiction/Category: _________

Where I bought, borrowed, or found the book: ______________

Main character(s) or subject: __________________________

My review and thoughts:

OVERALL RATING: Quality of writing ☆☆☆☆☆

Strength of characters ☆☆☆☆☆ Plot ☆☆☆☆☆

3. TITLE

Start date: ____________________ Finish date: ________________________

Author(s): ____

Publisher: _____________________________ Year published: ___________

Fiction/Genre: ____________ or Nonfiction/Category: _____________

Where I bought, borrowed, or found the book: _________________

Main character(s) or subject: _____________________________________

My review and thoughts:

OVERALL RATING: Quality of writing ☆☆☆☆☆

Strength of characters ☆☆☆☆☆ Plot ☆☆☆☆☆

4. TITLE

Start date: ____________________ Finish date: ________________________

Author(s): ____

Publisher: _____________________________ Year published: ___________

Fiction/Genre: ____________ or Nonfiction/Category: ______________

Where I bought, borrowed, or found the book: _____________________

Main character(s) or subject: _____________________________________

My review and thoughts:

OVERALL RATING: Quality of writing ☆☆☆☆☆

Strength of characters ☆☆☆☆☆ Plot ☆☆☆☆☆

5. TITLE

Start date: ____________ Finish date: ____________

Author(s): ____________

Publisher: ____________ Year published: ____________

Fiction/Genre: ____________ or Nonfiction/Category: ____________

Where I bought, borrowed, or found the book: ____________

Main character(s) or subject: ____________

My review and thoughts:

OVERALL RATING: Quality of writing ☆☆☆☆☆

Strength of characters ☆☆☆☆☆ Plot ☆☆☆☆☆

6. TITLE

Start date: ____________________ Finish date: ________________________

Author(s): ____

Publisher: _____________________________ Year published: __________

Fiction/Genre: ____________ or Nonfiction/Category: _____________

Where I bought, borrowed, or found the book: _____________________

Main character(s) or subject: ______________________________________

My review and thoughts:

OVERALL RATING: Quality of writing ☆☆☆☆☆

Strength of characters ☆☆☆☆☆ Plot ☆☆☆☆☆

7. TITLE

Start date: ____________________ Finish date: ______________________

Author(s): ____

Publisher: ______________________________ Year published: __________

Fiction/Genre: ____________ or Nonfiction/Category: _____________

Where I bought, borrowed, or found the book: ____________________

Main character(s) or subject: ___________________________________

My review and thoughts:

OVERALL RATING: Quality of writing ☆☆☆☆☆

Strength of characters ☆☆☆☆☆ Plot ☆☆☆☆☆

8. TITLE

Start date: ____________ Finish date: ____________

Author(s): ____________

Publisher: ____________ Year published: ____________

Fiction/Genre: ____________ or Nonfiction/Category: ____________

Where I bought, borrowed, or found the book: ____________

Main character(s) or subject: ____________

My review and thoughts:

OVERALL RATING: Quality of writing ☆☆☆☆☆

Strength of characters ☆☆☆☆☆ Plot ☆☆☆☆☆

9. TITLE

Start date: ______________ Finish date: ______________

Author(s): ______________

Publisher: ______________ Year published: ______________

Fiction/Genre: ______________ or Nonfiction/Category: ______________

Where I bought, borrowed, or found the book: ______________

Main character(s) or subject: ______________

My review and thoughts:

OVERALL RATING: Quality of writing ☆☆☆☆☆

Strength of characters ☆☆☆☆☆ Plot ☆☆☆☆☆

10. TITLE

Start date: ____________________ Finish date: ________________________

Author(s): ____

Publisher: _____________________________ Year published: ___________

Fiction/Genre: ____________ or Nonfiction/Category: _____________

Where I bought, borrowed, or found the book: _____________________

Main character(s) or subject: ______________________________________

My review and thoughts:

OVERALL RATING: Quality of writing ☆☆☆☆☆

Strength of characters ☆☆☆☆☆ Plot ☆☆☆☆☆

11. TITLE

Start date: ____________ Finish date: ____________

Author(s): ____________

Publisher: ____________ Year published: ____________

Fiction/Genre: ____________ or Nonfiction/Category: ____________

Where I bought, borrowed, or found the book: ____________

Main character(s) or subject: ____________

My review and thoughts:

OVERALL RATING: Quality of writing ☆☆☆☆☆

Strength of characters ☆☆☆☆☆ Plot ☆☆☆☆☆

12. TITLE

Start date: ____________________ Finish date: ________________________

Author(s): ____

Publisher: ______________________________ Year published: ___________

Fiction/Genre: ____________ or Nonfiction/Category: ______________

Where I bought, borrowed, or found the book: _____________________

Main character(s) or subject: _____________________________________

My review and thoughts:

OVERALL RATING: Quality of writing ☆☆☆☆☆

Strength of characters ☆☆☆☆☆ Plot ☆☆☆☆☆

13. TITLE

Start date: ______________ Finish date: ________________

Author(s): ____

Publisher: ____________________ Year published: ________

Fiction/Genre: _________ or Nonfiction/Category: __________

Where I bought, borrowed, or found the book: ____________

Main character(s) or subject: ________________________

My review and thoughts:

OVERALL RATING: Quality of writing ☆☆☆☆☆

Strength of characters ☆☆☆☆☆ Plot ☆☆☆☆☆

14. TITLE

Start date: ____________ Finish date: ____________

Author(s): ____________

Publisher: ____________ Year published: ____________

Fiction/Genre: ____________ or Nonfiction/Category: ____________

Where I bought, borrowed, or found the book: ____________

Main character(s) or subject: ____________

My review and thoughts:

OVERALL RATING: Quality of writing ☆☆☆☆☆

Strength of characters ☆☆☆☆☆ Plot ☆☆☆☆☆

15. TITLE

Start date: ____________________ Finish date: ________________________

Author(s): ____

Publisher: _____________________________ Year published: ___________

Fiction/Genre: ____________ or Nonfiction/Category: _____________

Where I bought, borrowed, or found the book: _____________________

Main character(s) or subject: _____________________________________

My review and thoughts:

OVERALL RATING: Quality of writing ☆☆☆☆☆

Strength of characters ☆☆☆☆☆ Plot ☆☆☆☆☆

16. TITLE

Start date: ____________ Finish date: ____________

Author(s): ____________

Publisher: ____________ Year published: ____________

Fiction/Genre: ____________ or Nonfiction/Category: ____________

Where I bought, borrowed, or found the book: ____________

Main character(s) or subject: ____________

My review and thoughts:

OVERALL RATING: Quality of writing ☆☆☆☆☆

Strength of characters ☆☆☆☆☆ Plot ☆☆☆☆☆

17. TITLE

Start date: ______________ Finish date: ______________

Author(s): ______________

Publisher: ______________ Year published: ______________

Fiction/Genre: ______________ or Nonfiction/Category: ______________

Where I bought, borrowed, or found the book: ______________

Main character(s) or subject: ______________

My review and thoughts:

OVERALL RATING: Quality of writing ☆☆☆☆☆

Strength of characters ☆☆☆☆☆ Plot ☆☆☆☆☆

18. TITLE

Start date: ____________ Finish date: ____________

Author(s): ____________

Publisher: ____________ Year published: ____________

Fiction/Genre: ____________ or Nonfiction/Category: ____________

Where I bought, borrowed, or found the book: ____________

Main character(s) or subject: ____________

My review and thoughts:

OVERALL RATING: Quality of writing ☆☆☆☆☆

Strength of characters ☆☆☆☆☆ Plot ☆☆☆☆☆

19. TITLE

Start date: ____________ Finish date: ____________

Author(s): ____________

Publisher: ____________ Year published: ____________

Fiction/Genre: ____________ or Nonfiction/Category: ____________

Where I bought, borrowed, or found the book: ____________

Main character(s) or subject: ____________

My review and thoughts:

OVERALL RATING: Quality of writing ☆☆☆☆☆

Strength of characters ☆☆☆☆☆ Plot ☆☆☆☆☆

20. TITLE

Start date: ____________ Finish date: ____________

Author(s): ____________

Publisher: ____________ Year published: ____________

Fiction/Genre: ____________ or Nonfiction/Category: ____________

Where I bought, borrowed, or found the book: ____________

Main character(s) or subject: ____________

My review and thoughts:

OVERALL RATING: Quality of writing ☆☆☆☆☆

Strength of characters ☆☆☆☆☆ Plot ☆☆☆☆☆

21. TITLE

Start date: ____________ Finish date: ____________

Author(s): ____________

Publisher: ____________ Year published: ____________

Fiction/Genre: ____________ or Nonfiction/Category: ____________

Where I bought, borrowed, or found the book: ____________

Main character(s) or subject: ____________

My review and thoughts:

OVERALL RATING: Quality of writing ☆☆☆☆☆

Strength of characters ☆☆☆☆☆ Plot ☆☆☆☆☆

22. TITLE

Start date: ____________ Finish date: ____________

Author(s): ____________

Publisher: ____________ Year published: ____________

Fiction/Genre: ____________ or Nonfiction/Category: ____________

Where I bought, borrowed, or found the book: ____________

Main character(s) or subject: ____________

My review and thoughts:

OVERALL RATING: Quality of writing ☆☆☆☆☆

Strength of characters ☆☆☆☆☆ Plot ☆☆☆☆☆

23. TITLE

Start date: ____________ Finish date: ____________

Author(s): ____________

Publisher: ____________ Year published: ____________

Fiction/Genre: ____________ or Nonfiction/Category: ____________

Where I bought, borrowed, or found the book: ____________

Main character(s) or subject: ____________

My review and thoughts:

OVERALL RATING: Quality of writing ☆☆☆☆☆

Strength of characters ☆☆☆☆☆ Plot ☆☆☆☆☆

24. TITLE

Start date: ____________________ Finish date: ____________________

Author(s): ____

Publisher: ____________________ Year published: __________

Fiction/Genre: __________ or Nonfiction/Category: __________

Where I bought, borrowed, or found the book: __________________

Main character(s) or subject: ______________________________

My review and thoughts:

OVERALL RATING: Quality of writing ☆☆☆☆☆

Strength of characters ☆☆☆☆☆ Plot ☆☆☆☆☆

25. TITLE

Start date: ____________ Finish date: ____________

Author(s): ____________

Publisher: ____________ Year published: ____________

Fiction/Genre: ____________ or Nonfiction/Category: ____________

Where I bought, borrowed, or found the book: ____________

Main character(s) or subject: ____________

My review and thoughts:

OVERALL RATING: Quality of writing ☆☆☆☆☆

Strength of characters ☆☆☆☆☆ Plot ☆☆☆☆☆

26. TITLE

Start date: ____________________ Finish date: ________________________

Author(s): ____

Publisher: ____________________________ Year published: ___________

Fiction/Genre: ____________ or Nonfiction/Category: _____________

Where I bought, borrowed, or found the book: _____________________

Main character(s) or subject: _____________________________________

My review and thoughts:

OVERALL RATING: Quality of writing ☆☆☆☆☆

Strength of characters ☆☆☆☆☆ Plot ☆☆☆☆☆

27. TITLE

Start date: ______________ Finish date: ______________

Author(s): ______________________________

Publisher: ______________ Year published: ________

Fiction/Genre: __________ or Nonfiction/Category: __________

Where I bought, borrowed, or found the book: ______________

Main character(s) or subject: ______________

My review and thoughts:

OVERALL RATING: Quality of writing ☆☆☆☆☆

Strength of characters ☆☆☆☆☆ Plot ☆☆☆☆☆

28. TITLE

Start date: ____________________ Finish date: ________________________

Author(s): ____

Publisher: _____________________________ Year published: ___________

Fiction/Genre: ____________ or Nonfiction/Category: ______________

Where I bought, borrowed, or found the book: ________________________

Main character(s) or subject: ______________________________________

My review and thoughts:

OVERALL RATING: Quality of writing ☆☆☆☆☆

Strength of characters ☆☆☆☆☆ Plot ☆☆☆☆☆

29. TITLE

Start date: ____________ Finish date: ____________

Author(s): ____________

Publisher: ____________ Year published: ____________

Fiction/Genre: ____________ or Nonfiction/Category: ____________

Where I bought, borrowed, or found the book: ____________

Main character(s) or subject: ____________

My review and thoughts:

OVERALL RATING: Quality of writing ☆☆☆☆☆

Strength of characters ☆☆☆☆☆ Plot ☆☆☆☆☆

30. TITLE

Start date: ______________ Finish date: ______________

Author(s): ______________

Publisher: ______________ Year published: ______

Fiction/Genre: __________ or Nonfiction/Category: __________

Where I bought, borrowed, or found the book: __________

Main character(s) or subject: ______________

My review and thoughts:

OVERALL RATING: Quality of writing ☆☆☆☆☆

Strength of characters ☆☆☆☆☆ Plot ☆☆☆☆☆

31. TITLE

Start date: ______________ Finish date: ______________

Author(s): ______________

Publisher: ______________ Year published: ______

Fiction/Genre: __________ or Nonfiction/Category: __________

Where I bought, borrowed, or found the book: ______________

Main character(s) or subject: ______________

My review and thoughts:

OVERALL RATING: Quality of writing ☆☆☆☆☆

Strength of characters ☆☆☆☆☆ Plot ☆☆☆☆☆

32. TITLE

Start date: ____________ Finish date: ____________

Author(s): ____________

Publisher: ____________ Year published: ____________

Fiction/Genre: ____________ or Nonfiction/Category: ____________

Where I bought, borrowed, or found the book: ____________

Main character(s) or subject: ____________

My review and thoughts:

OVERALL RATING: Quality of writing ☆☆☆☆☆

Strength of characters ☆☆☆☆☆ Plot ☆☆☆☆☆

33. TITLE

Start date: ____________ Finish date: ____________

Author(s): ____________

Publisher: ____________ Year published: ____________

Fiction/Genre: ____________ or Nonfiction/Category: ____________

Where I bought, borrowed, or found the book: ____________

Main character(s) or subject: ____________

My review and thoughts:

OVERALL RATING: Quality of writing ☆☆☆☆☆

Strength of characters ☆☆☆☆☆ Plot ☆☆☆☆☆

34. TITLE

Start date: ____________________ Finish date: ________________________

Author(s): ____

Publisher: ____________________________ Year published: ___________

Fiction/Genre: ____________ or Nonfiction/Category: _____________

Where I bought, borrowed, or found the book: ____________________

Main character(s) or subject: ____________________________________

My review and thoughts:

OVERALL RATING: Quality of writing ☆☆☆☆☆

Strength of characters ☆☆☆☆☆ Plot ☆☆☆☆☆

35. TITLE

Start date: ____________ Finish date: ____________

Author(s): ____________

Publisher: ____________ Year published: ____________

Fiction/Genre: ____________ or Nonfiction/Category: ____________

Where I bought, borrowed, or found the book: ____________

Main character(s) or subject: ____________

My review and thoughts:

OVERALL RATING: Quality of writing ☆☆☆☆☆

Strength of characters ☆☆☆☆☆ Plot ☆☆☆☆☆

36. TITLE

Start date: ____________ Finish date: ____________

Author(s): ____________

Publisher: ____________ Year published: ____________

Fiction/Genre: ____________ or Nonfiction/Category: ____________

Where I bought, borrowed, or found the book: ____________

Main character(s) or subject: ____________

My review and thoughts:

OVERALL RATING: Quality of writing ☆☆☆☆☆

Strength of characters ☆☆☆☆☆ Plot ☆☆☆☆☆

37. TITLE

Start date: ____________________ Finish date: ________________________

Author(s): ____

Publisher: ____________________________ Year published: ___________

Fiction/Genre: ____________ or Nonfiction/Category: _____________

Where I bought, borrowed, or found the book: ______________________

Main character(s) or subject: ________________________________

My review and thoughts:

OVERALL RATING: Quality of writing ☆☆☆☆☆

Strength of characters ☆☆☆☆☆ Plot ☆☆☆☆☆

38. TITLE

Start date: ____________ Finish date: ______________

Author(s): ______________________________________

Publisher: __________________ Year published: _______

Fiction/Genre: ________ or Nonfiction/Category: ________

Where I bought, borrowed, or found the book: ____________

Main character(s) or subject: _______________________

My review and thoughts:

OVERALL RATING: Quality of writing ☆☆☆☆☆

Strength of characters ☆☆☆☆☆ Plot ☆☆☆☆☆

39. TITLE

Start date: ____________ Finish date: ____________

Author(s): ____________

Publisher: ____________ Year published: ____________

Fiction/Genre: ____________ or Nonfiction/Category: ____________

Where I bought, borrowed, or found the book: ____________

Main character(s) or subject: ____________

My review and thoughts:

OVERALL RATING: Quality of writing ☆☆☆☆☆

Strength of characters ☆☆☆☆☆ Plot ☆☆☆☆☆

40. TITLE

Start date: ____________________ Finish date: ________________________

Author(s): ____

Publisher: _____________________________ Year published: ___________

Fiction/Genre: ____________ or Nonfiction/Category: ______________

Where I bought, borrowed, or found the book: _____________________

Main character(s) or subject: ______________________________________

My review and thoughts:

OVERALL RATING: Quality of writing ☆☆☆☆☆

Strength of characters ☆☆☆☆☆ Plot ☆☆☆☆☆

41. TITLE

Start date: ____________________ Finish date: ________________________

Author(s): ____

Publisher: _____________________________ Year published: ___________

Fiction/Genre: ____________ or Nonfiction/Category: _____________

Where I bought, borrowed, or found the book: _________________

Main character(s) or subject: _____________________________________

My review and thoughts:

OVERALL RATING: Quality of writing ☆☆☆☆☆

Strength of characters ☆☆☆☆☆ Plot ☆☆☆☆☆

42. TITLE

Start date: ____________ Finish date: ____________

Author(s): ____________

Publisher: ____________ Year published: ____________

Fiction/Genre: ____________ or Nonfiction/Category: ____________

Where I bought, borrowed, or found the book: ____________

Main character(s) or subject: ____________

My review and thoughts:

OVERALL RATING: Quality of writing ☆☆☆☆☆

Strength of characters ☆☆☆☆☆ Plot ☆☆☆☆☆

43. TITLE

Start date: ____________ Finish date: ____________

Author(s): ____________

Publisher: ____________ Year published: ____________

Fiction/Genre: ____________ or Nonfiction/Category: ____________

Where I bought, borrowed, or found the book: ____________

Main character(s) or subject: ____________

My review and thoughts:

OVERALL RATING: Quality of writing ☆☆☆☆☆

Strength of characters ☆☆☆☆☆ Plot ☆☆☆☆☆

44. TITLE

Start date: ________________ Finish date: ____________________

Author(s): ____

Publisher: ________________________ Year published: _________

Fiction/Genre: __________ or Nonfiction/Category: ___________

Where I bought, borrowed, or found the book: _________________

Main character(s) or subject: ______________________________

My review and thoughts:

OVERALL RATING: Quality of writing ☆☆☆☆☆

Strength of characters ☆☆☆☆☆ Plot ☆☆☆☆☆

45. TITLE

Start date: ________________ Finish date: ____________________

Author(s): ____

Publisher: ________________________ Year published: _________

Fiction/Genre: __________ or Nonfiction/Category: ___________

Where I bought, borrowed, or found the book: _________________

Main character(s) or subject: ______________________________

My review and thoughts:

OVERALL RATING: Quality of writing ☆☆☆☆☆

Strength of characters ☆☆☆☆☆ Plot ☆☆☆☆☆

46. TITLE

Start date: ____________ Finish date: ____________

Author(s): ____________

Publisher: ____________ Year published: ____________

Fiction/Genre: ____________ or Nonfiction/Category: ____________

Where I bought, borrowed, or found the book: ____________

Main character(s) or subject: ____________

My review and thoughts:

OVERALL RATING: Quality of writing ☆☆☆☆☆

Strength of characters ☆☆☆☆☆ Plot ☆☆☆☆☆

47. TITLE

Start date: ________________ Finish date: ____________________

Author(s): ____

Publisher: ________________________ Year published: _________

Fiction/Genre: __________ or Nonfiction/Category: ___________

Where I bought, borrowed, or found the book: _______________

Main character(s) or subject: ______________________________

My review and thoughts:

OVERALL RATING: Quality of writing ☆☆☆☆☆

Strength of characters ☆☆☆☆☆ Plot ☆☆☆☆☆

48. TITLE

Start date: ____________ Finish date: ______________

Author(s): ______________________________

Publisher: ________________ Year published: ________

Fiction/Genre: ________ or Nonfiction/Category: ________

Where I bought, borrowed, or found the book: ____________

Main character(s) or subject: ____________________

My review and thoughts:

OVERALL RATING: Quality of writing ☆☆☆☆☆

Strength of characters ☆☆☆☆☆ Plot ☆☆☆☆☆

49. TITLE

Start date: ____________________ Finish date: ________________________

Author(s): ____

Publisher: ____________________________ Year published: __________

Fiction/Genre: ____________ or Nonfiction/Category: ____________

Where I bought, borrowed, or found the book: __________________

Main character(s) or subject: ______________________________________

My review and thoughts:

OVERALL RATING: Quality of writing ☆☆☆☆☆

Strength of characters ☆☆☆☆☆ Plot ☆☆☆☆☆

50. TITLE

Start date: ____________________ Finish date: ________________________

Author(s): ____

Publisher: _____________________________ Year published: ___________

Fiction/Genre: ____________ or Nonfiction/Category: _____________

Where I bought, borrowed, or found the book: _____________________

Main character(s) or subject: _____________________________________

My review and thoughts:

OVERALL RATING: Quality of writing ☆☆☆☆☆

Strength of characters ☆☆☆☆☆ Plot ☆☆☆☆☆

51. TITLE

Start date: ____________ Finish date: ____________

Author(s): ____________

Publisher: ____________ Year published: ____________

Fiction/Genre: ____________ or Nonfiction/Category: ____________

Where I bought, borrowed, or found the book: ____________

Main character(s) or subject: ____________

My review and thoughts:

OVERALL RATING: Quality of writing ☆☆☆☆☆

Strength of characters ☆☆☆☆☆ Plot ☆☆☆☆☆

52. TITLE

Start date: ____________________ Finish date: ________________________

Author(s): ____

Publisher: _____________________________ Year published: ___________

Fiction/Genre: ____________ or Nonfiction/Category: ______________

Where I bought, borrowed, or found the book: _____________________

Main character(s) or subject: ______________________________________

My review and thoughts:

OVERALL RATING: Quality of writing ☆☆☆☆☆

Strength of characters ☆☆☆☆☆ Plot ☆☆☆☆☆

53. TITLE

Start date: ____________ Finish date: ____________

Author(s): ____________

Publisher: ____________ Year published: ____________

Fiction/Genre: ____________ or Nonfiction/Category: ____________

Where I bought, borrowed, or found the book: ____________

Main character(s) or subject: ____________

My review and thoughts:

OVERALL RATING: Quality of writing ☆☆☆☆☆

Strength of characters ☆☆☆☆☆ Plot ☆☆☆☆☆

54. TITLE

Start date: ______________ Finish date: ______________

Author(s): ______________

Publisher: ______________ Year published: ______________

Fiction/Genre: ______________ or Nonfiction/Category: ______________

Where I bought, borrowed, or found the book: ______________

Main character(s) or subject: ______________

My review and thoughts:

OVERALL RATING: Quality of writing ☆☆☆☆☆

Strength of characters ☆☆☆☆☆ Plot ☆☆☆☆☆

55. TITLE

Start date: ____________ Finish date: ____________

Author(s): ____________

Publisher: ____________ Year published: ____________

Fiction/Genre: ____________ or Nonfiction/Category: ____________

Where I bought, borrowed, or found the book: ____________

Main character(s) or subject: ____________

My review and thoughts:

OVERALL RATING: Quality of writing ☆☆☆☆☆

Strength of characters ☆☆☆☆☆ Plot ☆☆☆☆☆

56. TITLE

Start date: ____________________ Finish date: ________________________

Author(s): ____

Publisher: _____________________________ Year published: ___________

Fiction/Genre: ____________ or Nonfiction/Category: _____________

Where I bought, borrowed, or found the book: ______________________

Main character(s) or subject: ______________________________________

My review and thoughts:

OVERALL RATING: Quality of writing ☆☆☆☆☆

Strength of characters ☆☆☆☆☆ Plot ☆☆☆☆☆

57. TITLE

Start date: ________________ Finish date: ____________________

Author(s): ____

Publisher: ________________________ Year published: _________

Fiction/Genre: __________ or Nonfiction/Category: ___________

Where I bought, borrowed, or found the book: _________________

Main character(s) or subject: ________________________________

My review and thoughts:

OVERALL RATING: Quality of writing ☆☆☆☆☆

Strength of characters ☆☆☆☆☆ Plot ☆☆☆☆☆

58. TITLE

Start date: ________________ Finish date: ____________________

Author(s): ____

Publisher: ________________________ Year published: _________

Fiction/Genre: __________ or Nonfiction/Category: ___________

Where I bought, borrowed, or found the book: _________________

Main character(s) or subject: _______________________________

My review and thoughts:

OVERALL RATING: Quality of writing ☆☆☆☆☆

Strength of characters ☆☆☆☆☆ Plot ☆☆☆☆☆

59. TITLE

Start date: ______________ Finish date: ________________

Author(s): ____

Publisher: ____________________ Year published: ________

Fiction/Genre: _________ or Nonfiction/Category: ________

Where I bought, borrowed, or found the book: _______________

Main character(s) or subject: ___________________________

My review and thoughts:

OVERALL RATING: Quality of writing ☆☆☆☆☆

Strength of characters ☆☆☆☆☆ Plot ☆☆☆☆☆

60. TITLE

Start date: ____________________ Finish date: ________________________

Author(s): ____

Publisher: _____________________________ Year published: ___________

Fiction/Genre: ____________ or Nonfiction/Category: _____________

Where I bought, borrowed, or found the book: _____________________

Main character(s) or subject: ______________________________________

My review and thoughts:

OVERALL RATING: Quality of writing ☆☆☆☆☆

Strength of characters ☆☆☆☆☆ Plot ☆☆☆☆☆

61. TITLE

Start date: ____________________ Finish date: ________________________

Author(s): ____

Publisher: ____________________________ Year published: ___________

Fiction/Genre: ____________ or Nonfiction/Category: _____________

Where I bought, borrowed, or found the book: _____________________

Main character(s) or subject: _____________________________________

My review and thoughts:

OVERALL RATING: Quality of writing ☆☆☆☆☆

Strength of characters ☆☆☆☆☆ Plot ☆☆☆☆☆

62. TITLE

Start date: ______________ Finish date: ______________

Author(s): ______________________________

Publisher: ______________ Year published: ________

Fiction/Genre: __________ or Nonfiction/Category: __________

Where I bought, borrowed, or found the book: ______________

Main character(s) or subject: ______________________

My review and thoughts:

OVERALL RATING: Quality of writing ☆☆☆☆☆

Strength of characters ☆☆☆☆☆ Plot ☆☆☆☆☆

63. TITLE

Start date: ____________________ Finish date: ________________________

Author(s): ____

Publisher: _____________________________ Year published: ___________

Fiction/Genre: ____________ or Nonfiction/Category: ______________

Where I bought, borrowed, or found the book: ____________________

Main character(s) or subject: ______________________________________

My review and thoughts:

OVERALL RATING: Quality of writing ☆☆☆☆☆

Strength of characters ☆☆☆☆☆ Plot ☆☆☆☆☆

64. TITLE

Start date: ____________ Finish date: ____________

Author(s): ____________

Publisher: ____________ Year published: ____________

Fiction/Genre: ____________ or Nonfiction/Category: ____________

Where I bought, borrowed, or found the book: ____________

Main character(s) or subject: ____________

My review and thoughts:

OVERALL RATING: Quality of writing ☆☆☆☆☆

Strength of characters ☆☆☆☆☆ Plot ☆☆☆☆☆

65. TITLE

Start date: ____________________ Finish date: ________________________

Author(s): ____

Publisher: _____________________________ Year published: ___________

Fiction/Genre: ____________ or Nonfiction/Category: _____________

Where I bought, borrowed, or found the book: _____________________

Main character(s) or subject: _____________________________________

My review and thoughts:

OVERALL RATING: Quality of writing ☆☆☆☆☆

Strength of characters ☆☆☆☆☆ Plot ☆☆☆☆☆

66. TITLE

Start date: ____________________ Finish date: ________________________

Author(s): ____

Publisher: _____________________________ Year published: ___________

Fiction/Genre: ____________ or Nonfiction/Category: ______________

Where I bought, borrowed, or found the book: ____________________

Main character(s) or subject: ______________________________________

My review and thoughts:

OVERALL RATING: Quality of writing ☆☆☆☆☆

Strength of characters ☆☆☆☆☆ Plot ☆☆☆☆☆

67. TITLE

Start date: ____________________ Finish date: ________________________

Author(s): ____

Publisher: _____________________________ Year published: ___________

Fiction/Genre: ____________ or Nonfiction/Category: ______________

Where I bought, borrowed, or found the book: _____________________

Main character(s) or subject: ______________________________________

My review and thoughts:

OVERALL RATING: Quality of writing ☆☆☆☆☆

Strength of characters ☆☆☆☆☆ Plot ☆☆☆☆☆

68. TITLE

Start date: ____________ Finish date: ____________

Author(s): ____________

Publisher: ____________ Year published: ____________

Fiction/Genre: ____________ or Nonfiction/Category: ____________

Where I bought, borrowed, or found the book: ____________

Main character(s) or subject: ____________

My review and thoughts:

OVERALL RATING: Quality of writing ☆☆☆☆☆

Strength of characters ☆☆☆☆☆ Plot ☆☆☆☆☆

69. TITLE

Start date: ______________ Finish date: ______________

Author(s): ______________

Publisher: ______________ Year published: ______________

Fiction/Genre: ______________ or Nonfiction/Category: ______________

Where I bought, borrowed, or found the book: ______________

Main character(s) or subject: ______________

My review and thoughts:

OVERALL RATING: Quality of writing ☆☆☆☆☆

Strength of characters ☆☆☆☆☆ Plot ☆☆☆☆☆

70. TITLE

Start date: ____________ Finish date: ____________

Author(s): ____________

Publisher: ____________ Year published: ____________

Fiction/Genre: ____________ or Nonfiction/Category: ____________

Where I bought, borrowed, or found the book: ____________

Main character(s) or subject: ____________

My review and thoughts:

OVERALL RATING: Quality of writing ☆☆☆☆☆

Strength of characters ☆☆☆☆☆ Plot ☆☆☆☆☆

71. TITLE

Start date: ____________________ Finish date: ________________________

Author(s): ____

Publisher: ______________________________ Year published: ___________

Fiction/Genre: ____________ or Nonfiction/Category: _____________

Where I bought, borrowed, or found the book: _____________________

Main character(s) or subject: ________________________________

My review and thoughts:

OVERALL RATING: Quality of writing ☆☆☆☆☆

Strength of characters ☆☆☆☆☆ Plot ☆☆☆☆☆

72. TITLE

Start date: ______________ Finish date: ______________

Author(s): ______________

Publisher: ______________ Year published: ______________

Fiction/Genre: ______________ or Nonfiction/Category: ______________

Where I bought, borrowed, or found the book: ______________

Main character(s) or subject: ______________

My review and thoughts:

OVERALL RATING: Quality of writing ☆☆☆☆☆

Strength of characters ☆☆☆☆☆ Plot ☆☆☆☆☆

73. TITLE

Start date: ____________ Finish date: ____________

Author(s): ____________

Publisher: ____________ Year published: ____________

Fiction/Genre: ____________ or Nonfiction/Category: ____________

Where I bought, borrowed, or found the book: ____________

Main character(s) or subject: ____________

My review and thoughts:

OVERALL RATING: Quality of writing ☆☆☆☆☆

Strength of characters ☆☆☆☆☆ Plot ☆☆☆☆☆

74. TITLE

Start date: ____________ Finish date: ____________

Author(s): ____________

Publisher: ____________ Year published: ____________

Fiction/Genre: ____________ or Nonfiction/Category: ____________

Where I bought, borrowed, or found the book: ____________

Main character(s) or subject: ____________

My review and thoughts:

OVERALL RATING: Quality of writing ☆☆☆☆☆

Strength of characters ☆☆☆☆☆ Plot ☆☆☆☆☆

75. TITLE

Start date: ____________________ Finish date: ________________________

Author(s): ____

Publisher: _____________________________ Year published: ___________

Fiction/Genre: ____________ or Nonfiction/Category: ______________

Where I bought, borrowed, or found the book: _____________________

Main character(s) or subject: _____________________________________

My review and thoughts:

OVERALL RATING: Quality of writing ☆☆☆☆☆

Strength of characters ☆☆☆☆☆ Plot ☆☆☆☆☆

76. TITLE

Start date: ____________ Finish date: ____________

Author(s): ____________

Publisher: ____________ Year published: ____________

Fiction/Genre: ____________ or Nonfiction/Category: ____________

Where I bought, borrowed, or found the book: ____________

Main character(s) or subject: ____________

My review and thoughts:

OVERALL RATING: Quality of writing ☆☆☆☆☆

Strength of characters ☆☆☆☆☆ Plot ☆☆☆☆☆

77. TITLE

Start date: ____________ Finish date: ____________

Author(s): ____________

Publisher: ____________ Year published: ____________

Fiction/Genre: ____________ or Nonfiction/Category: ____________

Where I bought, borrowed, or found the book: ____________

Main character(s) or subject: ____________

My review and thoughts:

OVERALL RATING: Quality of writing ☆☆☆☆☆

Strength of characters ☆☆☆☆☆ Plot ☆☆☆☆☆

78. TITLE

Start date: ____________________ Finish date: ____________________

Author(s): ____

Publisher: ____________________________ Year published: __________

Fiction/Genre: ____________ or Nonfiction/Category: ____________

Where I bought, borrowed, or found the book: ____________________

Main character(s) or subject: ______________________________

My review and thoughts:

OVERALL RATING: Quality of writing ☆☆☆☆☆

Strength of characters ☆☆☆☆☆ Plot ☆☆☆☆☆

79. TITLE

Start date: ______________ Finish date: ______________

Author(s): ______________________________

Publisher: ______________ Year published: ________

Fiction/Genre: ________ or Nonfiction/Category: ________

Where I bought, borrowed, or found the book: ______________

Main character(s) or subject: ______________

My review and thoughts:

OVERALL RATING: Quality of writing ☆☆☆☆☆

Strength of characters ☆☆☆☆☆ Plot ☆☆☆☆☆

80. TITLE

Start date: ____________ Finish date: ____________

Author(s): ____________

Publisher: ____________ Year published: ____________

Fiction/Genre: ____________ or Nonfiction/Category: ____________

Where I bought, borrowed, or found the book: ____________

Main character(s) or subject: ____________

My review and thoughts:

OVERALL RATING: Quality of writing ☆☆☆☆☆

Strength of characters ☆☆☆☆☆ Plot ☆☆☆☆☆

81. TITLE

Start date: ______________ Finish date: ______________

Author(s): ______________________________

Publisher: ______________ Year published: ________

Fiction/Genre: __________ or Nonfiction/Category: __________

Where I bought, borrowed, or found the book: ______________

Main character(s) or subject: ______________

My review and thoughts:

OVERALL RATING: Quality of writing ☆☆☆☆☆

Strength of characters ☆☆☆☆☆ Plot ☆☆☆☆☆

82. TITLE

Start date: ____________ Finish date: ____________

Author(s): ____________

Publisher: ____________ Year published: ____________

Fiction/Genre: ____________ or Nonfiction/Category: ____________

Where I bought, borrowed, or found the book: ____________

Main character(s) or subject: ____________

My review and thoughts:

OVERALL RATING: Quality of writing ☆☆☆☆☆

Strength of characters ☆☆☆☆☆ Plot ☆☆☆☆☆

83. TITLE

Start date: ______________ Finish date: ______________

Author(s): ______________

Publisher: ______________ Year published: ______________

Fiction/Genre: ______________ or Nonfiction/Category: ______________

Where I bought, borrowed, or found the book: ______________

Main character(s) or subject: ______________

My review and thoughts:

OVERALL RATING: Quality of writing ☆☆☆☆☆

Strength of characters ☆☆☆☆☆ Plot ☆☆☆☆☆

84. TITLE

Start date: ______________ Finish date: ______________

Author(s): ______________

Publisher: ______________ Year published: ______________

Fiction/Genre: ______________ or Nonfiction/Category: ______________

Where I bought, borrowed, or found the book: ______________

Main character(s) or subject: ______________

My review and thoughts:

OVERALL RATING: Quality of writing ☆☆☆☆☆

Strength of characters ☆☆☆☆☆ Plot ☆☆☆☆☆

85. TITLE

Start date: ________________ Finish date: ____________________

Author(s): ____

Publisher: ________________________ Year published: _________

Fiction/Genre: __________ or Nonfiction/Category: ___________

Where I bought, borrowed, or found the book: _________________

Main character(s) or subject: ________________________________

My review and thoughts:

OVERALL RATING: Quality of writing ☆☆☆☆☆

Strength of characters ☆☆☆☆☆ Plot ☆☆☆☆☆

86. TITLE

Start date: ____________ Finish date: ____________

Author(s): ____________

Publisher: ____________ Year published: ____________

Fiction/Genre: ____________ or Nonfiction/Category: ____________

Where I bought, borrowed, or found the book: ____________

Main character(s) or subject: ____________

My review and thoughts:

OVERALL RATING: Quality of writing ☆☆☆☆☆

Strength of characters ☆☆☆☆☆ Plot ☆☆☆☆☆

87. TITLE

Start date: ____________ Finish date: ____________

Author(s): ____________

Publisher: ____________ Year published: ____________

Fiction/Genre: ____________ or Nonfiction/Category: ____________

Where I bought, borrowed, or found the book: ____________

Main character(s) or subject: ____________

My review and thoughts:

OVERALL RATING: Quality of writing ☆☆☆☆☆

Strength of characters ☆☆☆☆☆ Plot ☆☆☆☆☆

88. TITLE

Start date: ____________________ Finish date: ________________________

Author(s): ____

Publisher: ____________________________ Year published: ___________

Fiction/Genre: ____________ or Nonfiction/Category: _____________

Where I bought, borrowed, or found the book: ____________________

Main character(s) or subject: _____________________________________

My review and thoughts:

OVERALL RATING: Quality of writing ☆☆☆☆☆

Strength of characters ☆☆☆☆☆ Plot ☆☆☆☆☆

89. TITLE

Start date: ____________ Finish date: ____________

Author(s): ____________

Publisher: ____________ Year published: ____________

Fiction/Genre: ____________ or Nonfiction/Category: ____________

Where I bought, borrowed, or found the book: ____________

Main character(s) or subject: ____________

My review and thoughts:

OVERALL RATING: Quality of writing ☆☆☆☆☆

Strength of characters ☆☆☆☆☆ Plot ☆☆☆☆☆

90. TITLE

Start date: ____________ Finish date: ____________

Author(s): ____________

Publisher: ____________ Year published: ____________

Fiction/Genre: ____________ or Nonfiction/Category: ____________

Where I bought, borrowed, or found the book: ____________

Main character(s) or subject: ____________

My review and thoughts:

OVERALL RATING: Quality of writing ☆☆☆☆☆

Strength of characters ☆☆☆☆☆ Plot ☆☆☆☆☆

91. TITLE

Start date: ____________ Finish date: ____________

Author(s): ____________

Publisher: ____________ Year published: ____________

Fiction/Genre: ____________ or Nonfiction/Category: ____________

Where I bought, borrowed, or found the book: ____________

Main character(s) or subject: ____________

My review and thoughts:

OVERALL RATING: Quality of writing ☆☆☆☆☆

Strength of characters ☆☆☆☆☆ Plot ☆☆☆☆☆

92. TITLE

Start date: ____________ Finish date: ____________

Author(s): ____________

Publisher: ____________ Year published: ____________

Fiction/Genre: ____________ or Nonfiction/Category: ____________

Where I bought, borrowed, or found the book: ____________

Main character(s) or subject: ____________

My review and thoughts:

OVERALL RATING: Quality of writing ☆☆☆☆☆

Strength of characters ☆☆☆☆☆ Plot ☆☆☆☆☆

93. TITLE

Start date: ____________ Finish date: ______________

Author(s): ______________________________

Publisher: ________________ Year published: ________

Fiction/Genre: ________ or Nonfiction/Category: ________

Where I bought, borrowed, or found the book: ____________

Main character(s) or subject: ____________________

My review and thoughts:

OVERALL RATING: Quality of writing ☆☆☆☆☆

Strength of characters ☆☆☆☆☆ Plot ☆☆☆☆☆

94. TITLE

Start date: ____________ Finish date: ____________

Author(s): ____________

Publisher: ____________ Year published: ____________

Fiction/Genre: ____________ or Nonfiction/Category: ____________

Where I bought, borrowed, or found the book: ____________

Main character(s) or subject: ____________

My review and thoughts:

OVERALL RATING: Quality of writing ☆☆☆☆☆

Strength of characters ☆☆☆☆☆ Plot ☆☆☆☆☆

95. TITLE

Start date: ______________ Finish date: ______________

Author(s): ______________________________

Publisher: ______________ Year published: ________

Fiction/Genre: ________ or Nonfiction/Category: ________

Where I bought, borrowed, or found the book: ______________

Main character(s) or subject: ______________________

My review and thoughts:

OVERALL RATING: Quality of writing ☆☆☆☆☆

Strength of characters ☆☆☆☆☆ Plot ☆☆☆☆☆

96. TITLE

Start date: ____________________ Finish date: ________________________

Author(s): ____

Publisher: _____________________________ Year published: __________

Fiction/Genre: ____________ or Nonfiction/Category: _____________

Where I bought, borrowed, or found the book: _____________________

Main character(s) or subject: ______________________________________

My review and thoughts:

OVERALL RATING: Quality of writing ☆☆☆☆☆

Strength of characters ☆☆☆☆☆ Plot ☆☆☆☆☆

97. TITLE

Start date: ______________ Finish date: ______________

Author(s): ______________

Publisher: ______________ Year published: ______________

Fiction/Genre: ______________ or Nonfiction/Category: ______________

Where I bought, borrowed, or found the book: ______________

Main character(s) or subject: ______________

My review and thoughts:

OVERALL RATING: Quality of writing ☆☆☆☆☆

Strength of characters ☆☆☆☆☆ Plot ☆☆☆☆☆

98. TITLE

Start date: ____________ Finish date: ____________

Author(s): ____________

Publisher: ____________ Year published: ____________

Fiction/Genre: ____________ or Nonfiction/Category: ____________

Where I bought, borrowed, or found the book: ____________

Main character(s) or subject: ____________

My review and thoughts:

OVERALL RATING: Quality of writing ☆☆☆☆☆

Strength of characters ☆☆☆☆☆ Plot ☆☆☆☆☆

99. TITLE

Start date: ______________ Finish date: ______________

Author(s): ______________

Publisher: ______________ Year published: ______________

Fiction/Genre: ______________ or Nonfiction/Category: ______________

Where I bought, borrowed, or found the book: ______________

Main character(s) or subject: ______________

My review and thoughts:

OVERALL RATING: Quality of writing ☆☆☆☆☆

Strength of characters ☆☆☆☆☆ Plot ☆☆☆☆☆

100. TITLE

Start date: ____________________ Finish date: ________________________

Author(s): ____

Publisher: ______________________________ Year published: __________

Fiction/Genre: _____________ or Nonfiction/Category: ______________

Where I bought, borrowed, or found the book: ____________________

Main character(s) or subject: ________________________________

My review and thoughts:

OVERALL RATING: Quality of writing ☆☆☆☆☆

Strength of characters ☆☆☆☆☆ Plot ☆☆☆☆☆

24 BOOK CHALLENGES

"There is no Frigate like a Book
To take us Lands away."

—Emily Dickinson

24 BOOK CHALLENGES

☐ **1. A book written by someone on a different continent**

Title: ______________________________

Author(s): ______________________________

Publisher: ____________________ Year published: __________

Notes:

☐ **2. A book written before 1900**

Title: ______________________________

Author(s): ______________________________

Publisher: ______________ Year published: __________

Notes:

☐ 3. A book of poetry

Title: ______________________________

Author(s): ______________________________

Publisher: ____________________ Year published: __________

Notes:

☐ **4. A graphic novel**

Title: ______________________________

Author(s): ______________________________

Publisher: ____________________ Year published: __________

Notes:

☐ 5. A book set in wartime

Title: ______________________________

Author(s): ______________________________

Publisher: ____________________ Year published: __________

Notes:

☐ **6. A book recently turned into a movie or TV show**

Title: ______________________________

Author(s): ______________________________

Publisher: ____________________ Year published: __________

Notes:

☐ **7. A book set in a dystopian future**

Title: ______________________________

Author(s): ______________________________

Publisher: ______________________ Year published: ___________

Notes:

☐ **8. A book set in a time period you would like to visit**

Title: ______________________________

Author(s): ______________________________

Publisher: ____________________ Year published: __________

Notes:

☐ 9. A Pulitzer Prize–winning book

Title: ______________________________

Author(s): ______________________________

Publisher: ____________________ Year published: __________

Notes:

☐ **10. A book by or about someone you admire**

Title: ______________________________

Author(s): ______________________________

Publisher: ____________________ Year published: __________

Notes:

☐ 11. A book about religion or spirituality

Title: ____

Author(s): ____

Publisher: ____________________ Year published: __________

Notes:

☐ **12. A book of short stories**

Title: ______________________________

Author(s): ______________________________

Publisher: ____________________ Year published: __________

Notes:

☐ 13. A book set in a country you would like to visit

Title: ______________________________

Author(s): ______________________________

Publisher: ______________ Year published: __________

Notes:

☐ **14. A guilty-pleasure beach book**

Title: ______________________________

Author(s): ______________________________

Publisher: ________________ Year published: __________

Notes:

☐ **15. A book written the year you were born**

Title: ______________________________

Author(s): ______________________________

Publisher: ______________ Year published: ________

Notes:

☐ **16. A mystery**

Title: ______________________________

Author(s): ______________________________

Publisher: ____________________ Year published: __________

Notes:

☐ 17. A book about or narrated by a child

Title: ____________________

Author(s): ____________________

Publisher: ____________________ Year published: ____________

Notes:

☐ **18. A ghost story or scary book**

Title: ____

Author(s): ____

Publisher: ____________________ Year published: __________

Notes:

☐ 19. A memoir or biography

Title: ______________________________

Author(s): ______________________________

Publisher: ____________________ Year published: __________

Notes:

☐ **20. A book on politics**

Title: ____

Author(s): ____

Publisher: ____________________ Year published: __________

Notes:

☐ 21. A book about spies

Title: ______________________________

Author(s): ______________________________

Publisher: ________________ Year published: __________

Notes:

☐ **22. A romance**

Title: ______________________________

Author(s): ______________________________

Publisher: ______________________ Year published: ____________

Notes:

☐ 23. A fantasy

Title: ______________________________

Author(s): ______________________________

Publisher: ________________ Year published: __________

Notes:

☐ **24. A thriller**

Title: ____

Author(s): ____

Publisher: ________________________ Year published: ____________

Notes:

MY BOOK LISTS

"The reading of all good books is like conversation with the finest [people] of the past centuries."

—Descartes

MY BOOK LISTS

10 Favorite Books of All Time

1. Title: ______________________

   Author: ______________ Reason: ______________

2. Title: ______________________

   Author: ______________ Reason: ______________

3. Title: ______________________

   Author: ______________ Reason: ______________

4. Title: ______________________

   Author: ______________ Reason: ______________

5. Title: ______________________

   Author: ______________ Reason: ______________

6. Title: ______________________

   Author: ______________ Reason: ______________

7. Title: ______________________

   Author: ______________ Reason: ______________

8. Title: ______________________

   Author: ______________ Reason: ______________

9. Title: ______________________

   Author: ______________ Reason: ______________

10. Title: ______________________

    Author: ______________ Reason: ______________

MY BOOK LISTS

10 Favorite Characters

1. Title: ______________________

   Name of Character: ______________________

2. Title: ______________________

   Name of Character: ______________________

3. Title: ______________________

   Name of Character: ______________________

4. Title: ______________________

   Name of Character: ______________________

5. Title: ______________________

   Name of Character: ______________________

6. Title: ______________________

   Name of Character: ______________________

7. Title: ______________________

   Name of Character: ______________________

8. Title: ______________________

   Name of Character: ______________________

9. Title: ______________________

   Name of Character: ______________________

10. Title: ______________________

    Name of Character: ______________________

MY BOOK LISTS

10 Favorite Villains

1. Title: ______________________________

   Name of Character: ______________________________

2. Title: ______________________________

   Name of Character: ______________________________

3. Title: ______________________________

   Name of Character: ______________________________

4. Title: ______________________________

   Name of Character: ______________________________

5. Title: ______________________________

   Name of Character: ______________________________

6. Title: ______________________________

   Name of Character: ______________________________

7. Title: ______________________________

   Name of Character: ______________________________

8. Title: ______________________________

   Name of Character: ______________________________

9. Title: ______________________________

   Name of Character: ______________________________

10. Title: ______________________________

    Name of Character: ______________________________

MY BOOK LISTS

10 Favorite Book First Sentences

1. Title: ______________________________

   Sentence: ______________________________

2. Title: ______________________________

   Sentence: ______________________________

3. Title: ______________________________

   Sentence: ______________________________

4. Title: ______________________________

   Sentence: ______________________________

5. Title: ______________________________

   Sentence: ______________________________

6. Title: ______________________________

   Sentence: ______________________________

7. Title: ______________________________

   Sentence: ______________________________

8. Title: ______________________________

   Sentence: ______________________________

9. Title: ______________________________

   Sentence: ______________________________

10. Title: ______________________________

    Sentence: ______________________________

MY BOOK LISTS

10 Favorite Book Last Sentences

1. Title: ______________________

   Sentence: ______________________

2. Title: ______________________

   Sentence: ______________________

3. Title: ______________________

   Sentence: ______________________

4. Title: ______________________

   Sentence: ______________________

5. Title: ______________________

   Sentence: ______________________

6. Title: ______________________

   Sentence: ______________________

7. Title: ______________________

   Sentence: ______________________

8. Title: ______________________

   Sentence: ______________________

9. Title: ______________________

   Sentence: ______________________

10. Title: ______________________

    Sentence: ______________________

MY BOOK LISTS

10 Favorite Childhood Books

1. Title: ______________________________

   Author: ______________ Memory: ______________

2. Title: ______________________________

   Author: ______________ Memory: ______________

3. Title: ______________________________

   Author: ______________ Memory: ______________

4. Title: ______________________________

   Author: ______________ Memory: ______________

5. Title: ______________________________

   Author: ______________ Memory: ______________

6. Title: ______________________________

   Author: ______________ Memory: ______________

7. Title: ______________________________

   Author: ______________ Memory: ______________

8. Title: ______________________________

   Author: ______________ Memory: ______________

9. Title: ______________________________

   Author: ______________ Memory: ______________

10. Title: ______________________________

    Author: ______________ Memory: ______________

MY BOOK LISTS

10 Books I Would Bring to a Desert Island

1. Title: ______________________________

   Author: ______________ Reason: ______________

2. Title: ______________________________

   Author: ______________ Reason: ______________

3. Title: ______________________________

   Author: ______________ Reason: ______________

4. Title: ______________________________

   Author: ______________ Reason: ______________

5. Title: ______________________________

   Author: ______________ Reason: ______________

6. Title: ______________________________

   Author: ______________ Reason: ______________

7. Title: ______________________________

   Author: ______________ Reason: ______________

8. Title: ______________________________

   Author: ______________ Reason: ______________

9. Title: ______________________________

   Author: ______________ Reason: ______________

10. Title: ______________________________

    Author: ______________ Reason: ______________

MY BOOK LISTS

10 Favorite Books I Have Re-read

1. Title: ______________________________
   Author: ______________ Reason: ______________
2. Title: ______________________________
   Author: ______________ Reason: ______________
3. Title: ______________________________
   Author: ______________ Reason: ______________
4. Title: ______________________________
   Author: ______________ Reason: ______________
5. Title: ______________________________
   Author: ______________ Reason: ______________
6. Title: ______________________________
   Author: ______________ Reason: ______________
7. Title: ______________________________
   Author: ______________ Reason: ______________
8. Title: ______________________________
   Author: ______________ Reason: ______________
9. Title: ______________________________
   Author: ______________ Reason: ______________
10. Title: ______________________________
    Author: ______________ Reason: ______________

MY BOOK LISTS

10 Favorite Classics

1. Title: ____________________

   Author: __________ Reason: __________

2. Title: ____________________

   Author: __________ Reason: __________

3. Title: ____________________

   Author: __________ Reason: __________

4. Title: ____________________

   Author: __________ Reason: __________

5. Title: ____________________

   Author: __________ Reason: __________

6. Title: ____________________

   Author: __________ Reason: __________

7. Title: ____________________

   Author: __________ Reason: __________

8. Title: ____________________

   Author: __________ Reason: __________

9. Title: ____________________

   Author: __________ Reason: __________

10. Title: ____________________

    Author: __________ Reason: __________

MY BOOK LISTS

10 Favorite Books by Contemporary Authors

1. Title: ______________________________
   Author: ______________ Reason: ______________
2. Title: ______________________________
   Author: ______________ Reason: ______________
3. Title: ______________________________
   Author: ______________ Reason: ______________
4. Title: ______________________________
   Author: ______________ Reason: ______________
5. Title: ______________________________
   Author: ______________ Reason: ______________
6. Title: ______________________________
   Author: ______________ Reason: ______________
7. Title: ______________________________
   Author: ______________ Reason: ______________
8. Title: ______________________________
   Author: ______________ Reason: ______________
9. Title: ______________________________
   Author: ______________ Reason: ______________
10. Title: ______________________________
    Author: ______________ Reason: ______________

MY BOOK LISTS

10 Favorite Memoirs or Biographies

1. Title: ______________________

   Author: ____________ Reason: ____________

2. Title: ______________________

   Author: ____________ Reason: ____________

3. Title: ______________________

   Author: ____________ Reason: ____________

4. Title: ______________________

   Author: ____________ Reason: ____________

5. Title: ______________________

   Author: ____________ Reason: ____________

6. Title: ______________________

   Author: ____________ Reason: ____________

7. Title: ______________________

   Author: ____________ Reason: ____________

8. Title: ______________________

   Author: ____________ Reason: ____________

9. Title: ______________________

   Author: ____________ Reason: ____________

10. Title: ______________________

    Author: ____________ Reason: ____________

MY BOOK LISTS

10 Longest Books I Have Read

1. Title: ______________________________
   Author: ______________ Length: ______________
2. Title: ______________________________
   Author: ______________ Length: ______________
3. Title: ______________________________
   Author: ______________ Length: ______________
4. Title: ______________________________
   Author: ______________ Length: ______________
5. Title: ______________________________
   Author: ______________ Length: ______________
6. Title: ______________________________
   Author: ______________ Length: ______________
7. Title: ______________________________
   Author: ______________ Length: ______________
8. Title: ______________________________
   Author: ______________ Length: ______________
9. Title: ______________________________
   Author: ______________ Length: ______________
10. Title: ______________________________
    Author: ______________ Length: ______________

MY BOOK LISTS

10 Worst Books I Have Read

1. Title: ______________________________
   Author: ______________ Reason: ______________
2. Title: ______________________________
   Author: ______________ Reason: ______________
3. Title: ______________________________
   Author: ______________ Reason: ______________
4. Title: ______________________________
   Author: ______________ Reason: ______________
5. Title: ______________________________
   Author: ______________ Reason: ______________
6. Title: ______________________________
   Author: ______________ Reason: ______________
7. Title: ______________________________
   Author: ______________ Reason: ______________
8. Title: ______________________________
   Author: ______________ Reason: ______________
9. Title: ______________________________
   Author: ______________ Reason: ______________
10. Title: ______________________________
    Author: ______________ Reason: ______________

MY BOOK LISTS

10 Favorite Poems

1. Title: ____________________

   Author: ____________ Reason: ____________

2. Title: ____________________

   Author: ____________ Reason: ____________

3. Title: ____________________

   Author: ____________ Reason: ____________

4. Title: ____________________

   Author: ____________ Reason: ____________

5. Title: ____________________

   Author: ____________ Reason: ____________

6. Title: ____________________

   Author: ____________ Reason: ____________

7. Title: ____________________

   Author: ____________ Reason: ____________

8. Title: ____________________

   Author: ____________ Reason: ____________

9. Title: ____________________

   Author: ____________ Reason: ____________

10. Title: ____________________

    Author: ____________ Reason: ____________

MY BOOK LISTS

10 Favorite Movies or TV Shows Based on Books

1. Name of Book: ______________________

   Name of Movie or Show: ______________________

2. Name of Book: ______________________

   Name of Movie or Show: ______________________

3. Name of Book: ______________________

   Name of Movie or Show: ______________________

4. Name of Book: ______________________

   Name of Movie or Show: ______________________

5. Name of Book: ______________________

   Name of Movie or Show: ______________________

6. Name of Book: ______________________

   Name of Movie or Show: ______________________

7. Name of Book: ______________________

   Name of Movie or Show: ______________________

8. Name of Book: ______________________

   Name of Movie or Show: ______________________

9. Name of Book: ______________________

   Name of Movie or Show: ______________________

10. Name of Book: ______________________

    Name of Movie or Show: ______________________

MY BOOK LISTS

10 Funniest Books I Have Read

1. Title: ____________________

   Author: ____________ Reason: ____________

2. Title: ____________________

   Author: ____________ Reason: ____________

3. Title: ____________________

   Author: ____________ Reason: ____________

4. Title: ____________________

   Author: ____________ Reason: ____________

5. Title: ____________________

   Author: ____________ Reason: ____________

6. Title: ____________________

   Author: ____________ Reason: ____________

7. Title: ____________________

   Author: ____________ Reason: ____________

8. Title: ____________________

   Author: ____________ Reason: ____________

9. Title: ____________________

   Author: ____________ Reason: ____________

10. Title: ____________________

    Author: ____________ Reason: ____________

MY BOOK LISTS

10 Saddest Books I Have Read

1. Title: ____________________

   Author: ____________ Reason: ____________

2. Title: ____________________

   Author: ____________ Reason: ____________

3. Title: ____________________

   Author: ____________ Reason: ____________

4. Title: ____________________

   Author: ____________ Reason: ____________

5. Title: ____________________

   Author: ____________ Reason: ____________

6. Title: ____________________

   Author: ____________ Reason: ____________

7. Title: ____________________

   Author: ____________ Reason: ____________

8. Title: ____________________

   Author: ____________ Reason: ____________

9. Title: ____________________

   Author: ____________ Reason: ____________

10. Title: ____________________

    Author: ____________ Reason: ____________

MY BOOK LISTS

10 Scariest Books I Have Read

1. Title: ____________________

   Author: __________ Reason: __________

2. Title: ____________________

   Author: __________ Reason: __________

3. Title: ____________________

   Author: __________ Reason: __________

4. Title: ____________________

   Author: __________ Reason: __________

5. Title: ____________________

   Author: __________ Reason: __________

6. Title: ____________________

   Author: __________ Reason: __________

7. Title: ____________________

   Author: __________ Reason: __________

8. Title: ____________________

   Author: __________ Reason: __________

9. Title: ____________________

   Author: __________ Reason: __________

10. Title: ____________________

    Author: __________ Reason: __________

MY BOOK LISTS

10 Most Suspenseful Books I Have Read

1. Title: ______________________________

   Author: ______________ Reason: ______________

2. Title: ______________________________

   Author: ______________ Reason: ______________

3. Title: ______________________________

   Author: ______________ Reason: ______________

4. Title: ______________________________

   Author: ______________ Reason: ______________

5. Title: ______________________________

   Author: ______________ Reason: ______________

6. Title: ______________________________

   Author: ______________ Reason: ______________

7. Title: ______________________________

   Author: ______________ Reason: ______________

8. Title: ______________________________

   Author: ______________ Reason: ______________

9. Title: ______________________________

   Author: ______________ Reason: ______________

10. Title: ______________________________

    Author: ______________ Reason: ______________

MY BOOK LISTS

10 Most Romantic Books I Have Read

1. Title: ______________________

   Author: __________ Reason: __________

2. Title: ______________________

   Author: __________ Reason: __________

3. Title: ______________________

   Author: __________ Reason: __________

4. Title: ______________________

   Author: __________ Reason: __________

5. Title: ______________________

   Author: __________ Reason: __________

6. Title: ______________________

   Author: __________ Reason: __________

7. Title: ______________________

   Author: __________ Reason: __________

8. Title: ______________________

   Author: __________ Reason: __________

9. Title: ______________________

   Author: __________ Reason: __________

10. Title: ______________________

    Author: __________ Reason: __________

MY BOOK LISTS

10 Books That Taught Me the Most or Changed My Thinking

1. Title: ____________________

   Author: __________ Reason: __________

2. Title: ____________________

   Author: __________ Reason: __________

3. Title: ____________________

   Author: __________ Reason: __________

4. Title: ____________________

   Author: __________ Reason: __________

5. Title: ____________________

   Author: __________ Reason: __________

6. Title: ____________________

   Author: __________ Reason: __________

7. Title: ____________________

   Author: __________ Reason: __________

8. Title: ____________________

   Author: __________ Reason: __________

9. Title: ____________________

   Author: __________ Reason: __________

10. Title: ____________________

    Author: __________ Reason: __________

MY BOOK LISTS

10 Books by Authors Who I Would Invite to Dinner

1. Title: ______________________________

   Author: ______________ Reason: ______________

2. Title: ______________________________

   Author: ______________ Reason: ______________

3. Title: ______________________________

   Author: ______________ Reason: ______________

4. Title: ______________________________

   Author: ______________ Reason: ______________

5. Title: ______________________________

   Author: ______________ Reason: ______________

6. Title: ______________________________

   Author: ______________ Reason: ______________

7. Title: ______________________________

   Author: ______________ Reason: ______________

8. Title: ______________________________

   Author: ______________ Reason: ______________

9. Title: ______________________________

   Author: ______________ Reason: ______________

10. Title: ______________________________

    Author: ______________ Reason: ______________

MY BOOK LISTS

10 Books with the Coolest Titles

1. Title: ______________________________

   Author: ______________ Reason: ______________

2. Title: ______________________________

   Author: ______________ Reason: ______________

3. Title: ______________________________

   Author: ______________ Reason: ______________

4. Title: ______________________________

   Author: ______________ Reason: ______________

5. Title: ______________________________

   Author: ______________ Reason: ______________

6. Title: ______________________________

   Author: ______________ Reason: ______________

7. Title: ______________________________

   Author: ______________ Reason: ______________

8. Title: ______________________________

   Author: ______________ Reason: ______________

9. Title: ______________________________

   Author: ______________ Reason: ______________

10. Title: ______________________________

    Author: ______________ Reason: ______________

MY BOOK LISTS

10 Books with the Coolest Covers

1. Title: ____________________

   Author: __________ Reason: __________

2. Title: ____________________

   Author: __________ Reason: __________

3. Title: ____________________

   Author: __________ Reason: __________

4. Title: ____________________

   Author: __________ Reason: __________

5. Title: ____________________

   Author: __________ Reason: __________

6. Title: ____________________

   Author: __________ Reason: __________

7. Title: ____________________

   Author: __________ Reason: __________

8. Title: ____________________

   Author: __________ Reason: __________

9. Title: ____________________

   Author: __________ Reason: __________

10. Title: ____________________

    Author: __________ Reason: __________

BEST BOOK LISTS

PRIZEWINNERS AND CLASSICS

"To read well, that is, to read true books in a true spirit, is a noble exercise."

—Henry David Thoreau

The Modern Library—100 Best Novels

- ☐ 1. *Ulysses,* James Joyce
- ☐ 2. *The Great Gatsby,* F. Scott Fitzgerald
- ☐ 3. *A Portrait of the Artist As a Young Man,* James Joyce
- ☐ 4. *Lolita,* Vladimir Nabokov
- ☐ 5. *Brave New World,* Aldous Huxley
- ☐ 6. *The Sound and the Fury,* William Faulkner
- ☐ 7. *Catch-22,* Joseph Heller
- ☐ 8. *Darkness at Noon,* Arthur Koestler
- ☐ 9. *Sons and Lovers,* D. H. Lawrence
- ☐ 10. *The Grapes of Wrath,* John Steinbeck
- ☐ 11. *Under the Volcano,* Malcolm Lowry
- ☐ 12. *The Way of All Flesh,* Samuel Butler
- ☐ 13. *1984,* George Orwell
- ☐ 14. *I, Claudius,* Robert Graves
- ☐ 15. *To the Lighthouse,* Virginia Woolf
- ☐ 16. *An American Tragedy,* Theodore Dreiser
- ☐ 17. *The Heart Is a Lonely Hunter,* Carson McCullers
- ☐ 18. *Slaughterhouse-Five,* Kurt Vonnegut
- ☐ 19. *Invisible Man,* Ralph Ellison
- ☐ 20. *Native Son,* Richard Wright
- ☐ 21. *Henderson the Rain King,* Saul Bellow
- ☐ 22. *Appointment in Samarra,* John O'Hara
- ☐ 23. *U.S.A.* (trilogy), John Dos Passos
- ☐ 24. *Winesburg, Ohio,* Sherwood Anderson
- ☐ 25. *A Passage to India,* E. M. Forster
- ☐ 26. *The Wings of the Dove,* Henry James
- ☐ 27. *The Ambassadors,* Henry James
- ☐ 28. *Tender Is the Night,* F. Scott Fitzgerald
- ☐ 29. *Studs Lonigan* (trilogy), James T. Farrell
- ☐ 30. *The Good Soldier,* Ford Madox Ford
- ☐ 31. *Animal Farm,* George Orwell
- ☐ 32. *The Golden Bowl,* Henry James

- ☐ **33.** *Sister Carrie,* Theodore Dreiser
- ☐ **34.** *A Handful of Dust,* Evelyn Waugh
- ☐ **35.** *As I Lay Dying,* William Faulkner
- ☐ **36.** *All the King's Men,* Robert Penn Warren
- ☐ **37.** *The Bridge of San Luis Rey,* Thornton Wilder
- ☐ **38.** *Howards End,* E. M. Forster
- ☐ **39.** *Go Tell It on the Mountain,* James Baldwin
- ☐ **40.** *The Heart of the Matter,* Graham Greene
- ☐ **41.** *Lord of the Flies,* William Golding
- ☐ **42.** *Deliverance,* James Dickey
- ☐ **43.** *A Dance to the Music of Time* (series), Anthony Powell
- ☐ **44.** *Point Counter Point,* Aldous Huxley
- ☐ **45.** *The Sun Also Rises,* Ernest Hemingway
- ☐ **46.** *The Secret Agent,* Joseph Conrad
- ☐ **47.** *Nostromo,* Joseph Conrad
- ☐ **48.** *The Rainbow,* D. H. Lawrence
- ☐ **49.** *Women in Love,* D. H. Lawrence
- ☐ **50.** *Tropic of Cancer,* Henry Miller
- ☐ **51.** *The Naked and the Dead,* Norman Mailer
- ☐ **52.** *Portnoy's Complaint,* Philip Roth
- ☐ **53.** *Pale Fire,* Vladimir Nabokov
- ☐ **54.** *Light in August,* William Faulkner
- ☐ **55.** *On the Road,* Jack Kerouac
- ☐ **56.** *The Maltese Falcon,* Dashiell Hammett
- ☐ **57.** *Parade's End,* Ford Madox Ford
- ☐ **58.** *The Age of Innocence,* Edith Wharton
- ☐ **59.** *Zuleika Dobson,* Max Beerbohm
- ☐ **60.** *The Moviegoer,* Walker Percy
- ☐ **61.** *Death Comes for the Archbishop,* Willa Cather
- ☐ **62.** *From Here to Eternity,* James Jones
- ☐ **63.** *The Wapshot Chronicle,* John Cheever
- ☐ **64.** *The Catcher in the Rye,* J. D. Salinger
- ☐ **65.** *A Clockwork Orange,* Anthony Burgess
- ☐ **66.** *Of Human Bondage,* W. Somerset Maugham

- ☐ 67. *Heart of Darkness,* Joseph Conrad
- ☐ 68. *Main Street,* Sinclair Lewis
- ☐ 69. *The House of Mirth,* Edith Wharton
- ☐ 70. *The Alexandria Quartet,* Lawrence Durrell
- ☐ 71. *A High Wind in Jamaica,* Richard Hughes
- ☐ 72. *A House for Mr. Biswas,* V. S. Naipaul
- ☐ 73. *The Day of the Locust,* Nathanael West
- ☐ 74. *A Farewell to Arms,* Ernest Hemingway
- ☐ 75. *Scoop,* Evelyn Waugh
- ☐ 76. *The Prime of Miss Jean Brodie,* Muriel Spark
- ☐ 77. *Finnegans Wake,* James Joyce
- ☐ 78. *Kim,* Rudyard Kipling
- ☐ 79. *A Room with a View,* E. M. Forster
- ☐ 80. *Brideshead Revisited,* Evelyn Waugh
- ☐ 81. *The Adventures of Augie March,* Saul Bellow
- ☐ 82. *Angle of Repose,* Wallace Stegner
- ☐ 83. *A Bend in the River,* V. S. Naipaul
- ☐ 84. *The Death of the Heart,* Elizabeth Bowen
- ☐ 85. *Lord Jim,* Joseph Conrad
- ☐ 86. *Ragtime,* E. L. Doctorow
- ☐ 87. *The Old Wives' Tale,* Arnold Bennett
- ☐ 88. *The Call of the Wild,* Jack London
- ☐ 89. *Loving,* Henry Green
- ☐ 90. *Midnight's Children,* Salman Rushdie
- ☐ 91. *Tobacco Road,* Erskine Caldwell
- ☐ 92. *Ironweed,* William Kennedy
- ☐ 93. *The Magus,* John Fowles
- ☐ 94. *Wide Sargasso Sea,* Jean Rhys
- ☐ 95. *Under the Net,* Iris Murdoch
- ☐ 96. *Sophie's Choice,* William Styron
- ☐ 97. *The Sheltering Sky,* Paul Bowles
- ☐ 98. *The Postman Always Rings Twice,* James M. Cain
- ☐ 99. *The Ginger Man,* J. P. Donleavy
- ☐ 100. *The Magnificent Ambersons,* Booth Tarkington

The Modern Library—100 Best Books of Nonfiction

- ☐ 1. *The Education of Henry Adams,* Henry Adams
- ☐ 2. *The Varieties of Religious Experience,* William James
- ☐ 3. *Up from Slavery,* Booker T. Washington
- ☐ 4. *A Room of One's Own,* Virginia Woolf
- ☐ 5. *Silent Spring,* Rachel Carson
- ☐ 6. *Selected Essays,* 1917–1932, T. S. Eliot
- ☐ 7. *The Double Helix,* James D. Watson
- ☐ 8. *Speak, Memory,* Vladimir Nabokov
- ☐ 9. *The American Language,* H. L. Mencken
- ☐ 10. *The General Theory of Employment, Interest, and Money,* John Maynard Keynes
- ☐ 11. *The Lives of a Cell,* Lewis Thomas
- ☐ 12. *The Frontier in American History,* Frederick Jackson Turner
- ☐ 13. *Black Boy,* Richard Wright
- ☐ 14. *Aspects of the Novel,* E. M. Forster
- ☐ 15. *The Civil War,* Shelby Foote
- ☐ 16. *The Guns of August,* Barbara Tuchman
- ☐ 17. *The Proper Study of Mankind,* Isaiah Berlin
- ☐ 18. *The Nature and Destiny of Man,* Reinhold Niebuhr
- ☐ 19. *Notes of a Native Son,* James Baldwin
- ☐ 20. *The Autobiography of Alice B. Toklas,* Gertrude Stein
- ☐ 21. *The Elements of Style,* William Strunk and E. B. White
- ☐ 22. *An American Dilemma,* Gunnar Myrdal
- ☐ 23. *Principia Mathematica,* Alfred North Whitehead and Bertrand Russell
- ☐ 24. *The Mismeasure of Man,* Stephen Jay Gould
- ☐ 25. *The Mirror and the Lamp,* Meyer Howard Abrams
- ☐ 26. *The Art of the Soluble,* Peter B. Medawar
- ☐ 27. *The Ants,* Bert Hoelldobler and Edward O. Wilson
- ☐ 28. *A Theory of Justice,* John Rawls
- ☐ 29. *Art and Illusion,* Ernest H. Gombrich
- ☐ 30. *The Making of the English Working Class,* E. P. Thompson
- ☐ 31. *The Souls of Black Folk,* W. E. B. Du Bois
- ☐ 32. *Principia Ethica,* G. E. Moore

- ☐ **33.** *Philosophy and Civilization,* John Dewey
- ☐ **34.** *On Growth and Form,* D'arcy Thompson
- ☐ **35.** *Ideas and Opinions,* Albert Einstein
- ☐ **36.** *The Age of Jackson,* Arthur Schlesinger Jr.
- ☐ **37.** *The Making of the Atomic Bomb,* Richard Rhodes
- ☐ **38.** *Black Lamb and Grey Falcon,* Rebecca West
- ☐ **39.** *Autobiographies,* W. B. Yeats
- ☐ **40.** *Science and Civilization in China,* Joseph Needham
- ☐ **41.** *Goodbye to All That,* Robert Graves
- ☐ **42.** *Homage to Catalonia,* George Orwell
- ☐ **43.** *The Autobiography of Mark Twain,* Mark Twain
- ☐ **44.** *Children of Crisis,* Robert Coles
- ☐ **45.** *A Study of History,* Arnold J. Toynbee
- ☐ **46.** *The Affluent Society,* John Kenneth Galbraith
- ☐ **47.** *Present at the Creation,* Dean Acheson
- ☐ **48.** *The Great Bridge,* David McCullough
- ☐ **49.** *Patriotic Gore,* Edmund Wilson
- ☐ **50.** *Samuel Johnson,* Walter Jackson Bate
- ☐ **51.** *The Autobiography of Malcolm X,* Alex Haley and Malcolm X
- ☐ **52.** *The Right Stuff,* Tom Wolfe
- ☐ **53.** *Eminent Victorians,* Lytton Strachey
- ☐ **54.** *Working,* Studs Terkel
- ☐ **55.** *Darkness Visible,* William Styron
- ☐ **56.** *The Liberal Imagination,* Lionel Trilling
- ☐ **57.** *The Second World War,* Winston Churchill
- ☐ **58.** *Out of Africa,* Isak Dinesen
- ☐ **59.** *Jefferson and His Time,* Dumas Malone
- ☐ **60.** *In the American Grain,* William Carlos Williams
- ☐ **61.** *Cadillac Desert,* Marc Reisner
- ☐ **62.** *The House of Morgan,* Ron Chernow
- ☐ **63.** *The Sweet Science,* A. J. Liebling
- ☐ **64.** *The Open Society and Its Enemies,* Karl Popper
- ☐ **65.** *The Art of Memory,* Frances A. Yates
- ☐ **66.** *Religion and the Rise of Capitalism,* R. H. Tawney

☐ 67. *A Preface to Morals,* Walter Lippmann
☐ 68. *The Gate of Heavenly Peace,* Jonathan D. Spence
☐ 69. *The Structure of Scientific Revolutions,* Thomas S. Kuhn
☐ 70. *The Strange Career of Jim Crow,* C. Vann Woodward
☐ 71. *The Rise of the West,* William H. Mcneill
☐ 72. *The Gnostic Gospels,* Elaine Pagels
☐ 73. *James Joyce,* Richard Ellmann
☐ 74. *Florence Nightingale,* Cecil Woodham-Smith
☐ 75. *The Great War and Modern Memory,* Paul Fussell
☐ 76. *The City in History,* Lewis Mumford
☐ 77. *Battle Cry of Freedom,* James M. McPherson
☐ 78. *Why We Can't Wait,* Martin Luther King Jr.
☐ 79. *The Rise of Theodore Roosevelt,* Edmund Morris
☐ 80. *Studies in Iconology,* Erwin Panofsky
☐ 81. *The Face of Battle,* John Keegan
☐ 82. *The Strange Death of Liberal England,* George Dangerfield
☐ 83. *Vermeer,* Lawrence Gowing
☐ 84. *A Bright Shining Lie,* Neil Sheehan
☐ 85. *West with the Night,* Beryl Markham
☐ 86. *This Boy's Life,* Tobias Wolff
☐ 87. *A Mathematician's Apology,* G. H. Hardy
☐ 88. *Six Easy Pieces,* Richard P. Feynman
☐ 89. *Pilgrim at Tinker Creek,* Annie Dillard
☐ 90. *The Golden Bough,* James George Frazer
☐ 91. *Shadow and Act,* Ralph Ellison
☐ 92. *The Power Broker,* Robert A. Caro
☐ 93. *The American Political Tradition,* Richard Hofstadter
☐ 94. *The Contours of American History,* William Appleman Williams
☐ 95. *The Promise of American Life,* Herbert Croly
☐ 96. *In Cold Blood,* Truman Capote
☐ 97. *The Journalist and the Murderer,* Janet Malcolm
☐ 98. *The Taming of Chance,* Ian Hacking
☐ 99. *Operating Instructions,* Anne Lamott
☐ 100. *Melbourne,* Lord David Cecil

Pulitzer Prize for Fiction

[Years skipped indicate no awards given that year]

☐ **1918** *His Family,* Ernest Poole
☐ **1919** *The Magnificent Ambersons,* Booth Tarkington
☐ **1921** *The Age of Innocence,* Edith Wharton
☐ **1922** *Alice Adams,* Booth Tarkington
☐ **1923** *One of Ours,* Willa Cather
☐ **1924** *The Able McLaughlins,* Margaret Wilson
☐ **1925** *So Big,* Edna Ferber
☐ **1926** *Arrowsmith,* Sinclair Lewis (declined prize)
☐ **1927** *Early Autumn,* Louis Bromfield
☐ **1928** *The Bridge of San Luis Rey,* Thornton Wilder
☐ **1929** *Scarlet Sister Mary,* Julia Peterkin
☐ **1930** *Laughing Boy,* Oliver La Farge
☐ **1931** *Years of Grace,* Margaret Ayer Barnes
☐ **1932** *The Good Earth,* Pearl S. Buck
☐ **1933** *The Store,* Thomas Sigismund Stribling
☐ **1934** *Lamb in His Bosom,* Caroline Miller
☐ **1935** *Now in November,* Josephine Winslow Johnson
☐ **1936** *Honey in the Horn,* Harold L. Davis
☐ **1937** *Gone with the Wind,* Margaret Mitchell
☐ **1938** *The Late George Apley,* John Phillips Marquand
☐ **1939** *The Yearling,* Marjorie Kinnan Rawlings
☐ **1940** *The Grapes of Wrath,* John Steinbeck
☐ **1942** *In This Our Life,* Ellen Glasgow
☐ **1943** *Dragon's Teeth,* Upton Sinclair
☐ **1944** *Journey in the Dark,* Martin Flavin
☐ **1945** *A Bell for Adano,* John Hersey
☐ **1947** *All the King's Men,* Robert Penn Warren
☐ **1948** *Tales of the South Pacific,* James A. Michener
☐ **1949** *Guard of Honor,* James Gould Cozzens
☐ **1950** *The Way West,* A. B. Guthrie Jr.
☐ **1951** *The Town,* Conrad Richter

- ☐ **1952** *The Caine Mutiny,* Herman Wouk
- ☐ **1953** *The Old Man and the Sea,* Ernest Hemingway
- ☐ **1955** *A Fable,* William Faulkner
- ☐ **1956** *Andersonville,* MacKinlay Kantor
- ☐ **1958** *A Death in the Family,* James Agee (posthumous win)
- ☐ **1959** *The Travels of Jaimie McPheeters,* Robert Lewis Taylor
- ☐ **1960** *Advise and Consent,* Allen Drury
- ☐ **1961** *To Kill a Mockingbird,* Harper Lee
- ☐ **1962** *The Edge of Sadness,* Edwin O'Connor
- ☐ **1963** *The Reivers,* William Faulkner (posthumous win)
- ☐ **1965** *The Keepers of the House,* Shirley Ann Grau
- ☐ **1966** *The Collected Stories of Katherine Anne Porter,* Katherine Anne Porter
- ☐ **1967** *The Fixer,* Bernard Malamud
- ☐ **1968** *The Confessions of Nat Turner,* William Styron
- ☐ **1969** *House Made of Dawn,* N. Scott Momaday
- ☐ **1970** *The Collected Stories of Jean Stafford,* Jean Stafford
- ☐ **1972** *Angle of Repose,* Wallace Stegner
- ☐ **1973** *The Optimist's Daughter,* Eudora Welty
- ☐ **1975** *The Killer Angels,* Michael Shaara
- ☐ **1976** *Humboldt's Gift,* Saul Bellow
- ☐ **1977** No award given (*Roots,* Alex Haley, special Pulitzer Prize)
- ☐ **1978** *Elbow Room,* James Alan McPherson
- ☐ **1979** *The Stories of John Cheever,* John Cheever
- ☐ **1980** *The Executioner's Song,* Norman Mailer
- ☐ **1981** *A Confederacy of Dunces,* John Kennedy Toole (posthumous win)
- ☐ **1982** *Rabbit Is Rich,* John Updike
- ☐ **1983** *The Color Purple,* Alice Walker
- ☐ **1984** *Ironweed,* William Kennedy
- ☐ **1985** *Foreign Affairs,* Alison Lurie
- ☐ **1986** *Lonesome Dove,* Larry McMurtry
- ☐ **1987** *A Summons to Memphis,* Peter Taylor
- ☐ **1988** *Beloved,* Toni Morrison
- ☐ **1989** *Breathing Lessons,* Anne Tyler

- ☐ **1990** *The Mambo Kings Play Songs of Love,* Oscar Hijuelos
- ☐ **1991** *Rabbit at Rest,* John Updike
- ☐ **1992** *A Thousand Acres,* Jane Smiley
- ☐ **1993** *A Good Scent from a Strange Mountain,* Robert Olen Butler
- ☐ **1994** *The Shipping News,* E. Annie Proulx
- ☐ **1995** *The Stone Diaries,* Carol Shields
- ☐ **1996** *Independence Day,* Richard Ford
- ☐ **1997** *Martin Dressler: The Tale of an American Dreamer,* Steven Millhauser
- ☐ **1998** *American Pastoral,* Philip Roth
- ☐ **1999** *The Hours,* Michael Cunningham
- ☐ **2000** *Interpreter of Maladies,* Jhumpa Lahiri
- ☐ **2001** *The Amazing Adventures of Kavalier & Clay,* Michael Chabon
- ☐ **2002** *Empire Falls,* Richard Russo
- ☐ **2003** *Middlesex,* Jeffrey Eugenides
- ☐ **2004** *The Known World,* Edward P. Jones
- ☐ **2005** *Gilead,* Marilynne Robinson
- ☐ **2006** *March,* Geraldine Brooks
- ☐ **2007** *The Road,* Cormac McCarthy
- ☐ **2008** *The Brief Wondrous Life of Oscar Wao,* Junot Díaz
- ☐ **2009** *Olive Kitteridge,* Elizabeth Strout
- ☐ **2010** *Tinkers,* Paul Harding
- ☐ **2011** *A Visit From the Goon Squad,* Jennifer Egan
- ☐ **2013** *The Orphan Master's Son,* Adam Johnson
- ☐ **2014** *The Goldfinch,* Donna Tartt
- ☐ **2015** *All the Light We Cannot See,* Anthony Doerr
- ☐ **2016** *The Sympathizer,* Viet Thanh Nguyen
- ☐ **2017** *The Underground Railroad,* Colson Whitehead
- ☐ **2018** *Less,* Andrew Sean Greer
- ☐ **2019** *The Overstory,* Richard Powers
- ☐ **2020** *The Nickel Boys,* Colson Whitehead
- ☐ **2021** *The Night Watchman,* Louise Erdrich
- ☐ **2022** *The Netanyahus,* Joshua Cohen

The Booker Prize for Fiction

- ☐ **1997** *The God of Small Things,* Arundhati Roy
- ☐ **1969** *Something to Answer For,* P. H. Newby
- ☐ **1970** *The Elected Member,* Bernice Rubens
- ☐ **1970** (retrospective award) *Troubles,* J. G. Farrell
- ☐ **1971** *In a Free State,* V. S. Naipaul
- ☐ **1972** G., John Berger
- ☐ **1973** *The Siege of Krishnapur,* J. G. Farrell
- ☐ **1974** *The Conservationist,* Nadine Gordimer, and *Holiday,* Stanley Middleton
- ☐ **1975** *Heat and Dust,* Ruth Prawer Jhabvala
- ☐ **1976** *Saville,* David Storey
- ☐ **1977** *Staying On,* Paul Scott
- ☐ **1978** *The Sea, the Sea,* Iris Murdoch
- ☐ **1979** *Offshore,* Penelope Fitzgerald
- ☐ **1980** *Rites of Passage,* William Golding
- ☐ **1981** *Midnight's Children,* Salman Rushdie
- ☐ **1982** *Schindler's Ark (Schindler's List),* Thomas Keneally
- ☐ **1983** *Life & Times of Michael K,* J. M. Coetzee
- ☐ **1984** *Hotel du Lac,* Anita Brookner
- ☐ **1985** *The Bone People,* Keri Hulme
- ☐ **1986** *The Old Devils,* Kingsley Amis
- ☐ **1987** *Moon Tiger,* Penelope Lively
- ☐ **1988** *Oscar and Lucinda,* Peter Carey
- ☐ **1989** *The Remains of the Day,* Kazuo Ishiguro
- ☐ **1990** *Possession,* A. S. Byatt
- ☐ **1991** *The Famished Road,* Ben Okri
- ☐ **1992** *The English Patient,* Michael Ondaatje, and *Sacred Hunger,* Barry Unsworth
- ☐ **1993** *Paddy Clarke Ha Ha Ha,* Roddy Doyle
- ☐ **1994** *How Late It Was, How Late,* James Kelman
- ☐ **1995** *The Ghost Road,* Pat Barker

- ☐ **1996** *Last Orders,* Graham Swift
- ☐ **1998** *Amsterdam,* Ian McEwan
- ☐ **1999** *Disgrace,* J. M. Coetzee
- ☐ **2000** *The Blind Assassin,* Margaret Atwood
- ☐ **2001** *True History of the Kelly Gang,* Peter Carey
- ☐ **2002** *Life of Pi,* Yann Martel
- ☐ **2003** *Vernon God Little,* DBC Pierre
- ☐ **2004** *The Line of Beauty,* Alan Hollinghurst
- ☐ **2005** *The Sea,* John Banville
- ☐ **2006** *The Inheritance of Loss,* Kiran Desai
- ☐ **2007** *The Gathering,* Anne Enright
- ☐ **2008** *The White Tiger,* Aravind Adiga
- ☐ **2009** *Wolf Hall,* Hilary Mantel
- ☐ **2010** *The Finkler Question,* Howard Jacobson
- ☐ **2011** *The Sense of an Ending,* Julian Barnes
- ☐ **2012** *Bring Up the Bodies,* Hilary Mantel
- ☐ **2013** *The Luminaries,* Eleanor Catton
- ☐ **2014** *The Narrow Road to the Deep North,* Richard Flanagan
- ☐ **2015** *A Brief History of Seven Killings,* Marlon James
- ☐ **2016** *The Sellout,* Paul Beatty
- ☐ **2017** *Lincoln in the Bardo,* George Saunders
- ☐ **2018** *Milkman,* Anna Burns
- ☐ **2019** *The Testaments,* Margaret Atwood, and
  Girl, Woman, Other, Bernardine Evaristo
- ☐ **2020** *Shuggie Bain,* Douglas Stuart
- ☐ **2021** *The Promise,* Damon Galgut

BOOK CLUB

READING LIST

1. Title: ______________________________

   Author: ______________ Discussion Date: __________

2. Title: ______________________________

   Author: ______________ Discussion Date: __________

3. Title: ______________________________

   Author: ______________ Discussion Date: __________

4. Title: ______________________________

   Author: ______________ Discussion Date: __________

5. Title: ______________________________

   Author: ______________ Discussion Date: __________

6. Title: ______________________________

   Author: ______________ Discussion Date: __________

7. Title: ______________________________

   Author: ______________ Discussion Date: __________

8. Title: ______________________________

   Author: ______________ Discussion Date: __________

9. Title: ______________________________

   Author: ______________ Discussion Date: __________

10. Title: ______________________________

    Author: ______________ Discussion Date: __________

BOOK CLUB READING LIST

11. Title: ______

    Author: ______ Discussion Date: ______

12. Title: ______

    Author: ______ Discussion Date: ______

13. Title: ______

    Author: ______ Discussion Date: ______

14. Title: ______

    Author: ______ Discussion Date: ______

15. Title: ______

    Author: ______ Discussion Date: ______

16. Title: ______

    Author: ______ Discussion Date: ______

17. Title: ______

    Author: ______ Discussion Date: ______

18. Title: ______

    Author: ______ Discussion Date: ______

19. Title: ______

    Author: ______ Discussion Date: ______

20. Title: ______

    Author: ______ Discussion Date: ______

BOOK CLUB QUESTIONS

1. What did you like best about this book?
2. What did you like least about this book?
3. How did you find the quality of writing?
4. Which were your favorite characters?
5. Which were your least favorite characters?
6. Which character did you relate to the most?
7. If you were making a movie or television series based on this book, who would you cast in the starring roles?
8. What other books by this author have you read? Did you like them more or less than this book?
9. Would you read another book by this author? Why or why not?
10. What themes did the author emphasize throughout the book?
11. What did you think of the plot development?
12. What did you think of the book's ending?
13. How authentic were the characters and their dialogue?
14. How authentic is the culture, setting, or time period represented in the book?
15. What is your major take-away about the author's message?

BOOK CLUB NOTES

BOOK CLUB NOTES

WISH LIST OF BOOKS TO READ

"I read my eyes out and can't read half enough . . . The more one reads the more one sees we have to read."

—John Adams

WISH LIST OF BOOKS TO READ

WISH LIST OF BOOKS TO READ

WISH LIST OF BOOKS TO READ

WISH LIST OF BOOKS TO READ

WISH LIST OF BOOKS TO READ

WISH LIST OF BOOKS TO READ

WISH LIST OF BOOKS TO READ

WISH LIST OF BOOKS TO READ

WISH LIST OF BOOKS TO READ

WISH LIST OF BOOKS TO READ